Echo de Paris

Laurence Housman

Alpha Editions

This edition published in 2024

ISBN : 9789369057238

Design and Setting By
Alpha Editions
www.alphaedis.com
Email - info@alphaedis.com

Contents

Foreword

IN a book of political dialogues, published a year ago, I explained (perhaps unnecessarily) that they were entirely unauthentic—a personal interpretation, given in dramatic form, of certain minds and events that had gone to make
history.

But the dialogue which here follows differs from those, in that it has a solid basis in fact, and that I myself was a participant in the conversation which, as here recorded, is but a free rendering of what was then actually said.

And if it would interest any of my readers to know where these paraphrases of memory stand nearest to fact, they will find them in those passages dealing with the writings of Carlyle, the Scotsman's worship of success, and the theory of the complete life of the artist. Other references by the way were the bird with the Berkeleyan philosophy, and the novels of Mr. Benjamin Swift. The rest is my own development of the main theme, though it may well be that, here and there, I have remembered better than I know.

The scene, as regards its setting—the outside of a Paris restaurant—is true to history; and if, toward the end, a touch of drama has been introduced, the reader will understand that it is more symbolic than actual. The non-arriving guest, with the unreal name, did not, on that occasion, even begin to arrive. He was, nevertheless, a very real element in the tragic situation which I have tried to depict; and it is likely enough that there were more of his kind than one knew—that he was generic rather than individual.

My choice of initials to represent those who appear upon the scene—a convenient device for the better ordering of the printed page—was not made with any intention to disguise identity where that could be of interest; but it seemed better manners, in a scene where only one character really counted, to adopt the unobtrusive formula, except in speeches where the names occur naturally. The friendly "R.R." is dead, and will be easily identified; the rest are still living. And though, for the most part, they were listeners not speakers, I have no reason for leaving them out of a scene which, after nearly twenty-five years, I remember so well.

My original intention was to include this dialogue in my book of *Dethronements*; but I was warned by a good authority that if I did so the interest of my commentators would be largely diverted from the political theme to the personal; there was also a certain objection to including in a set of purely imaginary dialogues another which was so largely founded on fact. I decided, therefore, to let this other "dethronement" stand alone in its first appearing, as different in kind from the rest.

But though different, my reason for writing it was precisely the same. It is, like those others, a record of failure; and failures interest me more, generally, than success. If I am asked why, my answer is that they seem to reveal human nature more truly, and, on the whole, more encouragingly, than anything else in the world. The way a man faces failure is the best proof of him. What he has done before matters little, or only in a minor degree, if as the outcome of all, in the grip of final and irretrievable ruin, he retains the stature of a man. That places him far more truly than the verdicts of juries, or the judgment of contemporary society. Sometimes he may prove his worth more surely by failure than by success, sometimes may only just manage to hold his ground; but if he is able to do that without complaint or greedy self-justification, and without speaking bitterly of those who have compassed his downfall, even so something stands to his credit, and there is a balance on the right side.

And so, the longer I live, the more do failures attract me, making me believe not less in human nature, but more. There are financial vulgarians of our own day whom, in prison, one might find lovable—and so be brought nearer to the great common heart which, with its large tolerance for ill-doers in their gambling day of success, has found them lovable even when they were at their worst. For it is not only Art which holds up the mirror to Nature, or reflects most flatteringly the coarsest of its features. The British public flourishes its mirror, with all the self-satisfaction of a barber displaying his own handicraft, before characters of a certain type; and a man may follow a thoroughly vicious career with great success, so long as he does it in a thoroughly British way. But what a pity that the mirror should cease from its obsequious civility just when its hero, overwhelmed in failure and disgrace, becomes so much more worthy of study and deserving of sympathy than ever before.

And here, I suppose, lies the great difference between the mirror of Art and the mirror of popular opinion: the mirror of Art is not broken in a tantrum when the object becomes less acceptable to the public gaze. But the public is shocked in its sense of decency when it finds it has been looking at itself under an alias, applauding its own sorry features in the mask of success. The mask falls away, and there, instead, are the quite ordinary features of a poor human criminal, very like all the rest of us, if only it could be known: no wonder, then, that the mirror gets broken. In the mirror there is no such break: the interest holds on.

And so, from the non-popular standpoint, I had sufficient reason for putting on record my last meeting with so conspicuous a failure as Oscar Wilde. Our previous acquaintance, except by correspondence, had been very slight. Only once before had I met him at a friend's house. He was then at the height of his fame and success, and I an unknown beginner, still undecided whether to be book-illustrator or author. But I had recently published a short story, with illustrations of my own, in the *Universal Review*; and a few minutes after our introduction Mr. Wilde turned and, addressing me for the first time, said: "And when, pray, are we to have another work from your pen?"

Like most of his remarks, the enquiry was phrased with a certain decorative solemnity, in excess of what the occasion required; but the kindness and the courtesy of it were very real, and of course it pleased and encouraged me. I learned later that a certain descriptive phrase, "The smoke of their wood-fires lay upon the boughs, soft as the bloom upon a grape," had attracted him in my story; he had quoted it as beautiful, adding that one day he should use it himself, and, sure enough, in *The Picture of Dorian Grey*, I came upon it not long afterwards, slightly altered; and again I was pleased and complimented; for it meant that he had really liked something in my story, and had not praised merely to please.

I did not see him again to speak to, until we met in Paris some seven years later, the year before his death.

Upon his release from prison I had sent him my recently published book, *All-Fellows: seven legends of lower Redemption*, hoping that its title and contents would say something on my behalf, which, in his particular case, I very much wished to convey. A fortnight later a courteous and appreciative letter reached me from the south of France, telling me incidentally that by the same post had come a copy of *A Shropshire Lad*, sent with the good wishes of the author, whom he had never met. "Thus you and your brother," he wrote, "have given me a few moments of that rare thing called happiness."

From that time on I sent him each of my books as they appeared, and received letters of beautifully ornate criticism; and as I passed through Paris on my way back from Italy in the autumn of 1899, we met once more in the company of friends.

My memory of him upon that occasion inclines me to believe that those are right who maintain that as a personality he was more considerable than as a writer. The brilliancy of conversation is doubtfully reproduced in the cold medium of print, and I may have wholly failed to convey the peculiar and arresting quality of what, by word of mouth, sounded so well. But the impression left upon me from that occasion is that Oscar Wilde was incomparably the most accomplished talker I had ever met. The smooth-flowing utterance, sedate and self-possessed, oracular in tone, whimsical in substance, carried on without halt, or hesitation, or change of word, with the quiet zest of a man perfect at the game, and conscious that, for the moment at least, he was back at his old form again: this, combined with the pleasure, infectious to his listeners, of finding himself once more in a group of friends whose view of his downfall was not the world's view, made memorable to others besides myself a reunion more happily prolonged than this selected portion of it would indicate.

But what I admired most was the quiet, uncomplaining courage with which he accepted an ostracism against which, in his lifetime, there could be no appeal. To a man of his habits and temperament—conscious that the incentive to produce was gone with the popular applause which had been its recurrent stimulus—the outlook was utterly dark: life had already become a tomb. And it is as a "monologue d'outre tombe" that I recall his conversation that day; and whether it had any intrinsic value or no, it was at least a wonderful expression of that gift which he had for charming himself by charming others.

Among the many things he touched on that day (of which only a few disjointed sentences now remain to me), one note of enthusiasm I have always remembered, coming as it did so strangely from him, with his elaborate and artificial code of values, based mainly not on the beauty of human character, but on beauty of form—when, with a sudden warmth of word and tone, he praised Mrs. Gladstone for her greatness and gentleness of heart: "her beautiful and perfect charity" I think was the phrase he used, adding: "But then, she was always like that."

None of us knew her; but from that day on, the warmth and humility of his praise left an impression upon my mind, which a reading of her life only two years ago came to confirm. Perhaps—I like to think that it was possible—an expression of her "beautiful and perfect charity" had come to him personally, so making her stand differently in his eyes from the rest of the world.

Echo de Paris

A Study from Life

The echo is from as far back as the year 1899. It is late September. By the entrance of a café, on a street opening into the Place de l'Opera, three Englishmen sit waiting at a small table, relieved for the moment from the solicitations of the garçon anxious to serve them their aperitifs. It is all very well for the café to call itself the "Vieille Rose": no doubt by gaslight it lives charmingly up to its name; but seen in the noonday's glare, its interior upholsterings are unmistakably magenta. From the warm sunshade of its awning the street view is charming; and while one of the trio watches it benevolently with an accustomed eye, the other two, encountering Paris for the first time, find in its brisk movement the attraction of novelty. But it is a reversion to English habit which makes one of them presently look at his watch a little anxiously.

L.H. Is he generally so late as this?

R.R. Generally never as early.

L.H. You are sure you said the Café Vieille Rose?

R.R. (*with a disarming smile*). As well as I could, my dear L.H. I can't say it quite like you.

L.H. I don't pretend to talk French: hearing it spoken absorbs all my faculties.

R.R. Oh, but you should! They are so charming about it: they pretend to understand you.

L.H. Well, I did screw up courage to go to a French barber yesterday.

R.R. Ah! That explains it. I was wondering.

L.H. You might well. When I looked in the glass after he had finished me I saw myself no longer English, but Parisian.

R.R. (*enjoying himself*). No, L.H., no! Not Parisian, I assure you!—Alsatian.

L.H. No longer English was all that mattered: "tout à fait transformé," as I managed to say to the man. And he—magnificently: "Mais oui, Monsieur, c'était bien necessaire!" Is that what you call French politeness?

R.R. Rather the "amour propre" of the artist, I should say.

L.H. In this nation of artists one gets too much of it.

H.A. There isn't such a thing as a nation of artists. The French only appear so because they take a more transparent pride in themselves than we do. They haven't yet discovered that modesty is the best vanity.

R.R. Is that your own, Herbie, or did you get it from Oscar yesterday?

H.A. No. I didn't see him. I invented it as I got up this morning, meaning to let it occur as an impromptu. Now it's gone.

R.R. Oh, no. Say it again, my dear boy, say it again! We shall all be charmed: so will he.

L.H. Look; there he is! Who's with him?

R.R. Davray. I asked Davray to go and bring him, so as to make sure. You know him, don't you? You like him?

L.H. A Frenchman who can talk English always goes to my heart.

R.R. Davray is Anglomaniac: he not only talks it, he thinks it: signs himself "Henry," like an Englishman, and has read more of your books than I have.

L.H. One?

R.R. Don't be bitter, L.H. I read them—in the reviews—regularly.

(While they talk, a fiacre, disentangling itself from the traffic of the main thoroughfare, draws up at the newspaper-kiosk on the further side of the street, and discharges its occupants: one small, alert, and obviously a Frenchman; the other large and sedate, moving with a ponderous suavity, which gives him an air of importance, almost of dignity. But though he has still a presence, its magnificence has departed. Threading his way indolently across the traffic, his eye adventures toward the waiting group. Met by the studied cordiality of their greetings, his face brightens.)

R.R. Oscar, L.H. thinks you are late.

O.W. Thought I was going to be late, you mean, my dear Robbie. If I were, what matter? What are two minutes in three years of disintegrated lifetime? It is almost three years, is it not, since we missed seeing each other?

(This studied mention of a tragic lapse of time is not quite as happy as it would like to be, being too deliberate an understatement. The tactful "Robbie" hastens to restore the triviality suitable to the occasion.)

R.R. Oscar, when did you learn to cross streets? I have just seen you do it for the first time. In London you used to take a cab.

O.W. No, Robbie, the cab used to take me. But here the French streets are so polite; one gets to the right side of them without knowing it. (*He turns to L.H.*) How delightfully English of you to think that I was going to be late!

L.H. I thought you might have done as I am always doing—gone to the wrong place, or lost your way.

O.W. But that is impossible! In Paris one can lose one's time most delightfully; but one can never lose one's way.

H.A. With the Eiffel Tower as a guide, you mean?

O.W. Yes. Turn your back to that—you have all Paris before you. Look at it—Paris vanishes.

R.R. You might write a story about that, Oscar.

O.W. In natural history, Robbie, it has already been done. Travellers in South America tell of a bird which, if seen by you unawares, flies to hide itself. But if it has seen you first, then—by keeping its eye on you—it imagines that it remains invisible, and nothing will induce it to retreat. The bird-trappers catch it quite easily merely by advancing backwards. Now that, surely, is true philosophy. The bird, having once made you the object of its contemplation, has every right to think (as Bishop Berkeley did, I believe) that you have no independent existence. You are what you are—the bird says, and the Bishop says—merely because they have made you a subject of thought; if they did not think of you, you would not exist. And who knows?—they may be right. For, try as we may, we cannot get behind the appearance of things to the reality. And the terrible reason may be that there is no reality in things apart from their appearances.

H.D. You English are always talking what you think is philosophy, when we should only call it theology.

O.W. How typical of the French mind is that word "only"! But what else, my dear Davray, was the thought of the eighteenth century, so far as it went, but an attempt to bring Religion and Philosophy together in the bonds of holy matrimony?

R.R. The misalliance which produced the French Revolution.

O.W. Robbie, you must not be so brilliant before meals! Or do you wish to divert my appetite? May a guest who was supposed to be late enquire—when, precisely?

R.R. The situation, my dear Oscar, is of your own making. You insisted upon ortolans; L.H. telegraphed for them; they have only just arrived.

O.W. If they are still in their feathers, let them fly again! A flight of ortolans across Paris: how romantic, how unexplainable!

H.A. Oh, no! Let's wait for them, please! I want to taste one: I never have.

O.W. So young, and already so eager for disappointment! Why give up imagination? "Ortolan," the word, is far more beautiful than when it is made flesh. If you were wise you would learn life only by inexperience. That is what makes it always unexpected and delightful. Never to realize— that is the true ideal.

L.H. Still, one goes on liking plovers' eggs after eating them: at least, I do.

O.W. Ah, yes; an egg is always an adventure: it may be different. But you are right; there are a few things—like the Nocturnes of Chopin—which can repeat themselves without repetition. The genius of the artist preserves them from being ever quite realized. But it has to be done carelessly.

(There is a pause, while L.H., with due enquiry of each, orders the aperitifs.)

R.R. Oscar, why did you choose the "Vieille Rose"?

O.W. Will you believe me, Robbie, when I say—to match my complexion? I have never before seen it by daylight. Is it not a perfect parable of life, that such depravity by gaslight should become charming? Will our host allow us to have white wine as a corrective? An additional red might be dangerous.

(And with the colour-scheme of the approaching meal made safe, he continues to charm the ears of himself and of his listeners.)

I chose it also for another and a less selfish reason. It is here I once met a woman who was as charming as she was unfortunate, or as she would have been, but for the grace that was in her. To say that she was entirely without beauty is to put it mildly; but she accepted that gift of a blind God with so candid a benevolence, and cultivated it with so delicate an art, that it became a quality of distinction, almost of charm. She was the *belle amie* of a friend of mine, whose pity she had changed to love. He brought me here to meet her, telling me of the rare reputation she had acquired in this city of beautiful misalliances, as being a woman of whom nobody could possibly say that she was merely plain. And here, upon this spot, in the first few moments of our meeting, she challenged me, in the most charming manner possible, for that which a woman so rarely seeks to know—the truth about herself. "Tell me, Monsieur," she said—but no: it can only be told in

French: "Dites moi, Monsieur, si je ne suis pas la femme la plus laide à Paris?" And for once in my life I was able to please a woman merely by telling her the truth; and I replied, "Mais, Madame, dans tout le monde!"

R.R. A poem, in six words! What did she say?

O.W. What could she say, Robbie? She was delighted. To that impossible question which she had the courage to ask I had given the only impossible answer. Upon that we became friends. How much I have wished since that we could have met again. For the unbeautiful to have so much grace as to become charming is a secret that is worth keeping; and one the keeping of which I should have liked to watch. I would not have asked to know it for myself, for then it would no more be a mystery; but— merely to see her keeping it. In Paris (where almost everything is beautiful), they were very happy together. Now they are gone to America; and in that country, from which all sense of beauty has flown, perhaps she is no longer able to keep, as a secret, that which there would be no eyes to interpret. When I was in America, I did not dare to tell America the truth; but I saw it clearly even then—that the discovery of America was the beginning of the death of Art. But not yet; no, not yet! Whistler left America in order to remain an artist, and Mr. Sargent to become one, I believe.... But now, tell me of England: who are the new writers I ought to be reading, but have not?

L.H. Isn't to be told what you ought to like rather irritating?

O.W. But I did not say "like"; I said "read." There are many things one ought to read which one is not bound to like: Byron, Wordsworth—even Henry James, if Robbie will allow me to say so. But tell me whom you yourself find interesting. I shall, at least, be interested to know why. I have already had two books—from you and your brother—which have interested me.

L.H. Like you, as regards my own, I should be interested to know why?

O.W. Yours interested me—shall I confess?—partly because a few years ago it would have interested me so much less. For at that time, believing that I had discovered—that, in a way, I represented the symbol of my age, I was only interested in myself. Now, in an age to which I do not belong, I find myself interested in others. Robbie, who is the most sincere of flatterers, would have me believe that in this transfer of interest I am making a poor exchange. I am not sure. Till recently, absorbed in myself, I might have missed that new strange writer of things impossible in life, who writes under the name of Benjamin Swift. Ought I to have done so? His style has the gleam of a frozen fire. He writes like a sea-pirate driven by contrary winds to a vain search for tropical forests at the North Pole. Why does he look at life only in profile, as though, met face to face, it might mean death to him? Is he as mysterious, as unaccountable to himself, as he seems to others?

L.H. I don't know whether the fact that he is a well-to-do Scotsman, who finished his education at a German university, can be said to account for him. We have met, and I find him interesting. He reminds me, somehow, of a lion turned hermit, wearing a hair-shirt, and roaring into it to frighten out the fleas. In other words, he is full of contradictions, and revels in them even while they torment him.

O.W. A Scotsman? That explains everything. For a man to be both a genius and a Scotsman is the very stage for tragedy. He apparently perceives it. Generally they are unaware of it.

R.R. My dear Oscar, why cannot a Scotsman be a genius as comfortably as anyone else?

O.W. I ought to have said "artist": I meant artist. It is much easier for a Scotsman to be a genius than to be an artist. Mr. Gladstone, I believe, claimed to be a Scotsman whenever he stood for a Scottish constituency or spoke to a Scottish audience. The butter-Scotch flavour of it makes me believe it was true. There was no art in that; and yet how truly typical! It was always so successful....

Because, Robbie—to return to your question—your Scotsman believes only in success. How can a man, who regards success as the goal of life, be a true artist? God saved the genius of Robert Burns to poetry by driving him through drink to failure. Think what an appalling figure in literature a successful Burns would have been! He was already trying to write poems in polite English, which was about as ludicrous as for a polite Englishman to try to write poetry in the dialect of Burns. Riotous living and dying saved him from that last degradation of smug prosperity which threatened him.

L.H. But do you mean no artists are successful?

O.W. Incidentally; never intentionally. If they are, they remain incomplete. The artist's mission is to live the complete life: success, as an episode (which is all it can be); failure, as the real, the final end. Death, analysed to its resultant atoms—what is it but the vindication of failure: the getting rid for ever of powers, desires, appetites, which have been a lifelong embarrassment? The poet's noblest verse, the dramatist's greatest scene deal always with death; because the highest function of the artist is to make perceived the beauty of failure.

R.R. But have Scotsmen of genius been any more successful, in a wordly sense, than others? I seem to remember a few who failed rather handsomely.

O.W. Possibly. Providence is sometimes kinder to us than we are ourselves. But never was there a Scotsman of genius who survived his youth, who was not fatally compromised by his nationality. To fail and to die young is the only hope for a Scotsman who wishes to remain an artist. When, at the end of the eighteenth century, Scotland produced her second great writer of genius, she inspired him to a terrible betrayal (for which the tradespeople of literature still praise him)—to break his art on the wheel of commercial rectitude, to write books which became worse and worse, in order to satisfy his creditors! In Dante's *Purgatorio* there is nothing to equal the horror of it. But he succeeded; and Scotland, in consequence, is proud of him. I see by your faces that you all know the man I mean: one does not have to name him. Think of unhappy Sir Walter, writing his transcendent pot-boilers for no other reason than to wipe out bankruptcy! Bankruptcy, that beneficent fairy, who presents to all who trust her with their insolvency five, ten, fifteen, sometimes even nineteen shillings in the pound of what they owe to their creditors—to those usurious ones whose extortionate demands, recognized in other branches of the law, here get turned down. How much did she give me, Robbie?

R.R. An extension of time, Oscar. She hasn't done with you yet.

O.W. No; she does not dismiss the lover from her embraces while she has any hope of securing the restoration of his balance, or of discovering some deeper stain in his character. What touching devotion! She is the romantic figure of the money-market. But I believe—or at least I tell myself—that fewer Scotsmen go bankrupt than any other nationality. It is not, however, merely monetary success which seduces them; success, in all its aspects, has for them a baleful attraction. They succumb to it intellectually, morally, spiritually. On that Carlyle wrecked his chances of producing a permanent work of art greater than his *French Revolution*.

ALL. Carlyle?

O.W. I surprise you? Is that because we all know that Carlyle remained poor? So do misers. Carlyle was the greatest intellectual miser of the nineteenth century. In his prime he wrote his greatest work—the history of a failure—the French Revolution. The time came when, with all his powers matured, he stood equipped for the writing of his supreme masterpiece. There was no need to look far afield for a subject: it stood obvious awaiting him. After his French Revolution he should have written the life of Napoleon—the greatest success, the greatest failure that the world has ever known. He would have done it magnificently. What a spectacle for the world: the Man of Destiny receiving from the son of humble Scottish peasants his right measure of immortality! But because Carlyle was a Scotsman, he would not take for his hero the man whose life ended in failure: he could not bring himself to face the débâcle of Waterloo, the enduring ignominy and defeat of St. Helena. Had he been true to his art, he would have realized that St. Helena was the greatest theme of all—for an artist, the most completely significant in the whole of modern history. But because he had the soul of a Scotsman, because he worshipped success, he looked for his hero, and found him, in that most mean and despicable character, Frederick the Great: a man to whom heaven had given the powers of a supreme genius, and hell the soul of a commercial traveller with that unavailing itch for cultural gentility which Voltaire has exposed for us. On that mean theme he wrote his most voluminous work, and became, in the process, that skeleton in Mrs. Carlyle's cupboard which the world now knows.

You smile at me, Robbie, but believe me, in my own ruin I have found out this truth. The artist must live the complete life, must accept it as it comes and stands like an angel before him, with its drawn and two-edged sword. Great success, great failure—only so shall the artist see himself as he is, and through himself see others; only so shall he learn (as the artist must learn) the true meaning behind the appearance of things material, of life in general, and—more terrible still—the meaning of his own soul.

L.H. Why is a man's soul more terrible than life in general? Does not the greater include the less?

O.W. Because an epitome is always more terrible than a generalization. We do not see life in general steadily diminishing in force and vitality, or we do not realize it; the whole bulk is too great. But when a man really sees into himself, the process of diminution that is going on becomes apparent: he meets there a problem he cannot escape—a problem to which religion, and philosophy, and history can give no certain answer, however much they may pretend. As I sit here—with a few friends left to me; friends who, however faithful, their number must needs diminish—for I shall never make a new friend in my life, though perhaps a few after I die—as I sit here and look back, I realize that I have lived the complete life necessary to the artist: I have had great success, I have had great failure. I have learned the value of each; and I know now that failure means more—always must mean more than success. Why, then, should I complain? I do not mean that a certain infirmity of the flesh, or weakness of the will would not make me prefer that this should have happened to one of my friends—to one of you—rather than to myself; but admitting that, I still recognize that I have only at last come to the complete life which every artist must experience in order to join beauty to truth. I have come to see that St. Helena is, for a world which follows Cæsar and not Christ, the greatest place on earth next to Calvary. It is more neglected: men do not fight for it, they do not go out to conquer it in weary generations of disastrous crusades, like those which did so much to destroy for Catholic Europe the true significance of Christianity. But it is there; and only when men begin to fight for it, as a thing desirable and precious to possess, only then will its spiritual significance change, and its value diminish.

If I could write what I have been saying to you, if I could hope to interest others, as I seem to have interested you, I would; but the world will not listen to me—now. It is strange—I never thought it possible before—to regret that one has too much leisure: leisure which I used so to lack, when I myself was a creator of beautiful things.

L.H. But you told me, in your last letter, that you were writing something?

O.W. I told you that I was going to write something: I tell everybody that. It is a thing one can repeat each day, meaning to do it the next. But in my heart—that chamber of leaden echoes—I know that I never shall. It is enough that the stories have been invented, that they actually exist; that I have been able, in my own mind, to give them the form which they demand.

R.R. If you won't write them, Oscar, you might at least tell them.

O.W. You have heard them all, Robbie.

R.R. The others have not.

O.W. My dear Robbie, you are not nearly artful enough; but you are very kind. I will tell you one of my stories presently. Let us go on talking till the appropriate moment makes it more possible.... Is it I, or is it the ortolans that are still keeping us here? I do not mind; I would only like to know.

R.R. To tell you the truth, Oscar, the ortolans were merely a delicate excuse. We are now waiting for the most perfectly forgetful, and the most regularly unpunctual person that any of us know. Do you mind if I cling for five minutes more to my belief that he really intends to meet us?

O.W. Not at all; a charming experiment. Forgetfulness is a great gift. While he exercises it, we have more time for being happy where we are than we should otherwise have allowed ourselves. Who is our benefactor?

R.R. I thought you might like to meet Harvey Jerrold again. I was keeping it behind the ortolans as a surprise for you.

(The name has evoked a look of eager, almost of startled, pleasure; and response comes with animation.)

O.W. My dear Robbie; but how inventive of you! What a finishing touch to a circle which already seemed complete! I did not know that he was here.

R.R. He only arrived last night. I 'phoned to his hotel and left a message for him asking him to join us. This morning he sent word that he would come.

O.W. *(with just a shade of doubt in his tone)*. Did you tell him who we all were?

R.R. I only said "friends." He knows all of us.

O.W. If he has not, in the exercise of his gift, forgotten some of us. That—as I remember him—is possible.

R.R. He can't have forgotten you, at any rate, considering it was you who published his first plays for him. Or did you only write them?

O.W. Ah! but he has done so much better since. Suppose he were now ashamed of them. He was one of those—true artists—who make a reputation before they do anything. That is the right way to begin; but few have the courage to persevere. It is so difficult. Yet he, of course, is the most complete artist who is able to remain perfect—doing nothing.

R.R. I have heard you say that before. But for the sake of the others won't you explain it? Your explanations are so much more illuminating than your statements, you know.

O.W. I may have said the same thing before, Robbie. (It requires a friend to tell one so!) But my explanation, I am sure, will always be different. And yet the one which comes at this moment seems only too obvious. The greatest work of the imagination, for an artist, is to create first himself, then his public. The writing of my plays and my poems was never difficult: because they belonged to me, they came at call. But to make my own public was a labour of Hercules. That is what I did first. The effort lay in the fact that while one appeared to be doing nothing, one was actually prostrated by the exertion. I have known what it is to come back from a week-end—one of those ordeals by tattle which the stately homes of England provide for the passing guest—almost literally at death's door, from which nothing but hermetic seclusion, until the week-end following, enabled me to escape. One of my doctors called it "heart-strain," the other "brain-fag." It was really both. I remember once, on a Monday morning, missing an unreasonably early train, and having to return for four hours to the bosom of a ducal family, when its exhibition hours were over. It was a charnel house: the bones of its skeleton rattled: the ghosts gibbered and moaned.

Time remained motionless. I was haunted. I could never go there again. I had seen what man is never meant to see—the sweeping up of the dust on which the footfall of departing pleasure has left its print. There for two days I had been creating my public: the two days given by God to the Jewish and the Christian world for rest; and from that breaking of the sabbath, creator and created were equally exhausted. The breath of life I had so laboriously breathed into their nostrils they were getting rid of again, returning to native clay. And yet how few understand what a life of heroism is that of an artist when he is producing—not his art, but the receptacle which is to contain it. That, dear friends, is why the world is to the artist so tragic. It is always a struggle. The artist may possibly for a while mould the world; but if the world moulds him, he has failed to become an artist, though he may have succeeded in acquiring the Scotch accent.

L.H. You spoke just now of the artist creating a public for the appreciation of his work; can he not also create other artists? Would not that be the ideal aim?

O.W. Ideal, but impossible. You cannot create an artist; you can only invent one—and it always remains a fiction. Artists—God's last creation, secret recipients of the Word of Life—continue to create themselves. But invention is often tried as a substitute. I remember, years ago, Hermann Vezin inventing an actress who was to be a second Rachel. For years and years he continued to invent her, telling us what to expect. Then one day he produced her....

R.R. (*after allowing the rhetorical pause its due weight*). What happened? I don't remember.

O.W. On the day he produced her, she ceased to exist.

R.R. You mean she didn't arrive?

O.W. Her arrival was a departure: the stage was her terminus. Engines whistled; the uproar became frightful. She ran to Brighton without stopping; and, I believe, still dies there.

L.H. Was she so bad, then, after all?

O.W. She may have been almost a genius; who can tell? The fatal mistake was when Hermann Vezin began inventing her. What would happen to an actress, however great, who came upon the stage bejewelled with the names of Sarah, Rachel, Ristori, Siddons? Probability becomes violated; the sense of the theatre is destroyed. When that happens all is over. Hermann Vezin should have held his tongue till the gods themselves applauded. But he lacked faith. The worst thing you can do for a person of genius is to help him: that way lies destruction. I have had many devoted helpers—and you see the result. Only once did I help a man who was also a genius. I have never forgiven myself.

R.R. Oscar, you are perfectly absurd!

O.W. (*with a glance of genuine affection*). But I have forgiven *you*, Robbie.

L.H. What happened?

O.W. To the man I helped? He never told me; and I would not ask. When we met afterwards, he had so greatly changed that, though I recognized him, he failed to recognize me. He became a Roman Catholic, and died at the age of twenty-three, a great artist—with half the critics and all the moralists still hating him. A charming person!

L.H. How often one hears that said, as though it were the final summing up of a man's life and character—covering everything.

O.W. But surely it is so. What is more fundamental, more inalienable from a man's personality, than charm? He may lose his looks; he may lose his character; but in almost every case that I have known—in spite of adverse circumstances—the charm remains, like the gift of a fairy godmother: something which cannot be got rid of. A person who has charm has the secret of life; but does not know what the secret is—he himself being the secret. For in this wonderful turning world we can know other people by their differences—as I know all of you; but we can never know ourselves. Matthew Arnold, a fine but a very mistaken poet, was always trying to do the most impossible thing of all—to know himself. And that is why sometimes, in the middle of his most beautiful poems, he left off being the poet and became the school inspector.

L.H. I thought you said that the artist must know himself in order to know others?

O.W. Never! You misunderstood me. "See himself" is what I said; and, seeing himself naked but not ashamed, learn the terrible meaning of his own soul—how it exists to torment and divide him against himself, but always as a stranger within his gates, remote, inscrutable, unnatural. For this thing, which he can never understand, goes deeper than the consciousness of self—it is something primitive, atavistic, fierce, and savage with a fanatical faith in gods whom this world tries no longer to believe in, but still fears, lest they should become true. When news of Matthew Arnold's death came to Robert Louis Stevenson in Samoa, he said (for he was a Scotsman with a fine sense of humour): "How dreadful! He won't like God." You smile; and yet there was a very real truth in it. The theology of Matthew Arnold was a terrible mistake; it arose out of that insistence on trying to know himself: he wanted also to know God. And just as trying to know yourself savours of social snobbery—being an attempt to know the person you think the most important in the world, so in the other attempt there is a certain spiritual snobbery. It is surely quite sufficient that He should know us, without any pretended recognition on our part, which, in any case, would be futile. For if a man cannot know his own soul with real understanding, still less can he know with real understanding that which directs its ministry of pain—that constant intolerable reminder that we can never, unless we would choose only to be dust, belong separately and entirely to ourselves. Man's destiny is to be haunted; however deserted of his fellows, he is never for a moment alone. Matthew Arnold, in one of his poems, made that beautiful but ridiculous statement which appeals to us, perhaps, as true because we would so much like it to be true:

Yes, in this sea of life enisled,

We mortal millions live alone!

We don't: we live with a familiar who is a stranger, always eating out of our hand, always defrauding us of the joys of life while denying us the reason. And we never know from day to day whether that stranger is going to murder us in cold blood, or make us become saints.

R.R. Why not both? To me they sound almost synonymous.

O.W. Robbie, you must not interrupt me, saying clever, sensible things like that: you put me out. People who want to say merely what is sensible should say it to themselves before they come down to breakfast in the morning, never after.

L.H. That was when Lewis Carroll's "White Queen" used to practise telling herself all the things she knew to be impossible.

R.R. I always thought that meant saying her prayers.

O.W. But saying prayers, Robbie, is always possible. It is only the answer to prayer that is impossible. Prayer must never be answered: if it is, it ceases to be prayer, and becomes a correspondence. If we ask for our daily bread and it is given us as manna was given to the Israelites in the wilderness, it is merely an invitation to dinner reversed. How much more devotional the exercise becomes when we know that our food comes to us from quite mundane sources, irrespective of prayer.

H.D. But your prayer then becomes merely a superstition.

O.W. Not at all: a compliment—a spiritual courtesy which one may surely hope is appreciated in the proper place. I do not say it derisively. There is a proper place for the appreciation of everything. And perhaps it is only in heaven—and in hell—that art, now so generally despised, will receive the appreciation that is due to it.

H.A. In heaven, yes; but why in hell?

O.W. Why in hell? I must tell you one of my stories.

(A grave smile passes from face to face, as the friends lean forward attentively to listen; for they know that this born story-teller only tells them when, for the moment, life contents him.)

In hell, among all the brave company that is ever to be found there of lovers, and fair ladies, and men of learning, and poets, and astrologers, amid all the ceaseless movement of doomed bodies, tossing and turning to be rid of the torment of their souls, one woman sat alone and smiled. She had the air of a listener, ever with lifted head and eyes raised, as though some voice from above were attracting her.

"Who is that woman?" enquired a new-comer, struck by the strange loveliness of her face, with its look the meaning of which he could not read, "the one with the smooth, ivory limbs, and the long hair falling down over her arms to the hands resting upon her lap. She is the only soul whose eyes are ever looking aloft. What skeleton does she keep in the cupboard of God up yonder?"

He had not finished speaking before one made haste to answer, a man who carried in his hand a wreath of withered leaves. "They say," he said, "that once on earth she was a great singer, with a voice like stars falling from a clear sky. So when doom came for her, God took her voice and cast it forth to the eternal echoes of the spheres, finding it too beautiful a thing to let die. Now she hears it with recognition, and remembering how once it was her own, shares still the pleasure which God takes in it. Do not speak to her, for she believes that she is in heaven."

And when the man, bearing the wreath of withered leaves, had finished, "No," said another, "that is not her story."

"What then?"

"It is this," he said, as the man with the withered wreath turned away: "On earth a poet made his song of her, so that her name became eternally wedded to his verse, which still rings on the lips of men. Now she lifts her head and can hear his praise of her sounded wherever language is spoken. That is her true story."

"And the poet?" asked the new-comer. "Did she love him well?"

"So little," replied the other, "that here and now she passes him daily and does not recognize his face."

"And he?"

The other laughed, and answered: "It is he who just now told you that tale concerning her voice, continuing here the lies which he used to make about her when they two were together on earth."

But the new-comer said, "If he is able to give happiness in hell, how can what he says be a lie?"

(There is an appreciative pause: no one speaks: from those listening faces no word of praise is necessary. Once more the speaker has secured the homage of his fellow men; and so, forgetting for a while the pit that life has digged for him, continues to narrate to his friends the stories which he will never write.)

Since that has appealed to you, I will tell you another.... Once there was a young man, so beautiful of mind that all who heard him wished to be of his company; so beautiful of form——

(In the middle of a sentence he pauses, as he sees advancing—though the others, intent only on him, do not—a young man, graceful in person, indolent in motion, who, with a light nonchalant air, meets and lets go the glances of strangers as they pass. From these, as he draws near, his eye turns toward the group seated at the out-door table under the sun-bright awning, and becomes fixed and attentive. Glance meets glance, holds for a moment, till that of the younger man is withdrawn. Without any change of countenance he slightly deflects his course and passes on. In the face they are watching, the friends see a quick change: the colour goes, the look of quiet expectation ends abruptly, as though sight had stopped dead. But it is with his accustomed deliberation of tone that at last he resumes speaking.)

Ah, no; that is a story of which I have forgotten the end: or else it has forgotten me. No matter; I will tell you another. This is one that has only just occurred to me; and I am not quite sure yet what the end of it will be. But it is there waiting. You and I will listen to this story together, as I tell it for the first time.

This shall be called "The Story of the Man who sold his Soul."

A certain traveller, passing through the streets of a great city, came there upon a man whose countenance indicated a grief which he could not fathom. The traveller, being a curious student of the human heart, stopped him and said: "Sir, what is this grief which you carry before the eyes of all men, so grievous that it cannot be hidden, yet so deep that it cannot be read?"

The man answered: "It is not I who grieve so greatly; it is my soul, of which I cannot get rid. And my soul is more sorrowful than death, for it hates me, and I hate it."

The traveller said: "If you will sell your soul to me, you can be well rid of it." The other answered: "Sir, how can I sell you my soul?" "Surely," replied the traveller, "you have but to agree to sell me your soul at its full price; then, when I bid it, it comes to me. But every soul has its true price; and only at that, neither at more nor at less, can it be bought."

Then said the other: "At what price shall I sell you this horrible thing, my soul?"

The traveller answered: "When a man first sells his own soul he is like that other betrayer; therefore its price should be thirty pieces of silver. But after that, if it passes to other hands, its value becomes small; for to others the souls of their fellow men are worth very little."

So for thirty pieces of silver the man sold his soul; and the traveller took it and departed.

Presently the man, having no soul, found that he could do no sin. Though he stretched out his arms to sin, sin would not come to him. "You have no soul," said sin, and passed him by. "Wherefore should I come to you? I have no profit in a man that has no soul?"

Then the man without a soul became very miserable, for though his hands touched what was foul they remained clean, and though his heart longed for wickedness, it remained pure; and when he thirsted to dip his lips in fire, they remained cool.

Therefore a longing to recover his soul took hold of him, and he went through the world searching for the traveller to whom he had sold it, that he might buy it back and again taste sin in his own body.

After a long time the traveller met him; but hearing his request he laughed and said: "After a while your soul wearied me and I sold it to a Jew for a smaller sum than I paid for it."

"Ah!" cried the man, "if you had come to me I would have paid more." The traveller answered: "You could not have done that; a soul cannot be bought or sold but at its just price. Your soul came to be of small value in my keeping; so to be rid of it I sold it to the first comer for considerably less money than I paid in the beginning."

So parting from him the man continued his quest, wandering over the face of the earth and seeking to recover his lost soul. And one day as he sat in the bazaar of a certain town a woman passed him, and looking at him said: "Sir, why are you so sad? It seems to me there can be no reason for such sadness." The man answered: "I am sad because I have no soul, and am seeking to find it."

The other said: "Only the other night I bought a soul that had passed through so many hands that it had become dirt-cheap; but it is so poor a thing I would gladly be rid of it. Yet I bought it for a mere song; and a soul can only be sold at its just price; how, then, shall I be able to sell it again—for what is worth less than a song? And it was but a light song that I sang over the wine-cup to the man who sold it me."

When the other heard that, he cried: "It is my own soul! Sell it to me, and I will give you all that I possess!"

The woman said: "Alas, I did but pay for it with a song, and I can but sell it again at its just price. How then can I be rid of it, though it cries and laments to be set free?"

The man without a soul laid his head to the woman's breast, and heard within it the captive soul whimpering to be set free, to return to the body it had lost. "Surely," he said, "it is my own soul! If you will sell it to me I will give you my body, which is worth less than a song from your lips."

So, for his body, the other sold to him the soul that whimpered to be set free to return to its own place. But so soon as he received it he rose up aghast: "What have you done?" he cried, "and what is this foul thing that has possession of me? For this soul that you have given me is not *my* soul!"

The woman laughed and said: "Before you sold your soul into captivity it was a free soul in a free body; can you not recognize it now it comes to you from the traffic of the slave-market? So, then, your soul has the greater charity, since it recognizes and returns to you, though you have sold your body miserably into bondage!"

And thus it was that the man had to buy back, at the cost of his body, the soul which he let go for thirty pieces of silver.

(With occasional pauses imposed for effect, but without any hesitation or change in the choice of word, the ordered narrative has run its course. But in spite of the decorative form, and the decorative modulations of tone, there is an under-current of passion; and his friends, undeceived by that quiet deliberateness of speech, know that the speaker is greatly moved. And so, at the end, there is a pause while nobody speaks. At the kiosk opposite a newsboy arrives, and delivers a bundle of papers to the woman in charge. Over her is an announcement to the Englishman, in his native tongue, that his own papers are there on sale. From the restaurant comes a garçon charged with a message, and wishing to have instructions. The two,

who have shared in the arrangement, exchange glances interrogatively; R.R. looks at his watch and nods. L.H. signs to the garçon who has served the aperitifs.)

R.R. Let us go in to lunch. Jerrold is not coming; he has forgotten us.

O.W. Not all of us, Robbie. He came, but he has gone again.

(*They all look at him in astonishment; and, for a moment, nobody speaks. Then:*)

R.R. Came? *Here*, do you mean?

O.W. Looking as young and charming as ever. But, as soon as he looked at me, I saw he had entirely forgotten me.

(*There is nothing possible to be said. L.H. makes haste to pay for the aperitifs; and with the anxiety of an Englishman, unpractised in foreign ways, to do what is right for the reputation of his country in a strange land, he puts down an additional pour-boire, five bronze pieces in all, to correspond to the number who have been served. With grave apologetic politeness his guest lays an arresting hand upon his arm; and (while the garçon whisks away the douceur with cheerful alacrity) instructs him for future occasions.*)

O.W. My dear L.H., you should not do that! The Frenchman, for these casual services, gives what you call a penny. The Englishman gives what some of them call "tuppence"; not because he does not know that the Frenchman's penny is sufficient, but because he is an Englishman. If you give more than that the waiter only thinks that you do not know where you are.

L.H. (*who has a weakness for putting himself in the right, even in quite small matters.*) Ah, yes, Mr. Wilde, that may be, but here, at St. Helena, one tips the waiters differently.

(*It is touching to see what pleasure that foolish but fortunate little "mot" has given to the man for whom it was designed. They have all now risen; and their next move will be to the tabled interior, where pleasant courses are awaiting them. But the forward movement is delayed; and it is with a curious air of finality, as though already taking his leave, that O.W. speaks.*)

O.W. My friends, we have had a wonderful hour together. I have been very happy. Excuse me: I am going across to get an English paper. The woman at the kiosk, who sells them, is a charming character: she compliments my accent by pretending to think that I am French. Go in: I beg you not to wait for me.

(*They see him cross the street, with his accustomed air of leisurely deliberation—a little amused to notice how the vehement traffic has to pause and make way for him. At the kiosk he and the woman exchange words and smiles. He lifts his hat and turns away.)*

L.H. *(startled)*. He's not coming back?

R.R. Harvey Jerrold wants kicking. Poor Oscar!

H.A. Shall I go after him?

R.R. No, no! Let him go. We understand.

(And they all stand and watch, as he passes slowly down the street, till he disappears in the crowd.)

Footnote

TWENTY years after a man's death is usually a sufficient time to compose, in their proper unimportance, the prejudices and enmities which have surrounded his career. But in this particular case, I suppose, it has hardly done so; and the man who was so greatly over-rated by his own following, during those ten years of literary and social triumph which made him the vogue, was, in the ten years after, as carefully under-rated, not because the quality of his work had proved itself poor and ephemeral, but because of something that he had done.

The blight which fell on his literary reputation was about as sensible in its application as it would have been for historians to deny that Marlborough was a great general because he peculated and took bribes, or that Mahomet was a great religious leader because he had a number of wives, or that David was a great poet because he preferred the love of Jonathan to the love of women. In which last-named absurdity of critical inconsequence we have something very much to the point; and it is upon that point, and because the world has been so unintelligently slow in seizing it, that I am moved to write this footnote to my dialogue, with which, in subject, it has so little to do.

Always, so long as it stays remembered, the name of Oscar Wilde is likely to carry with it a shadowy implication of that strange pathological trouble which caused his downfall. And whatever else may be said for or against the life of promiscuous indulgence he appears to have led, his downfall did at least this great service to humanity, that—by the sheer force of notoriety—it made the "unmentionable" mentionable; and marks the dividing of the ways between the cowardice and superstitious ignorance with which the problem had been treated even by sociologists and men of science, and the fearless analysis of origins and causes which has now become their more reputable substitute.

Obscurantists may still insist on treating as an acquired depravity what medical research has now proved to be an involuntary or congenital deflection from a "normality" which exact science finds it harder and harder to define. But in spite of these surviving resistances to the formation of a new social conscience, intelligence is at work, and to-day it is no longer eccentric or disreputable to insist that the whole problem shall henceforth be studied and treated from the medical, rather than from the criminal standpoint; so that in future, whatever limitation of reticence or segregation society decides to impose on men whose tendencies are ineradicably homo-sexual, the treatment shall be health-giving in character and purpose, carrying with it no social or moral damnation of those who, in the vast majority of cases, have been made what they are by forces outside their own volition, either at their birth or in early infancy.

The comical ignorance and ineptitude of which quite brilliant minds are capable in regard to a matter that they wish to relegate to mental obscurity, was well exemplified in the remarks made to me on this subject, only ten years ago, by one who ranked then as now among the most eminent of British bacteriologists. He had been told, he said, that homo-sexuality came from meat-eating; and his solution of the problem was to have all homo-sexuals put to death. But the subject, he went on to say, did not interest him; nor did he propose to give the meat-eaters (of whom he himself was one) any warning of their pathological danger, or of his proposed remedy for the pathological condition to which their meat-eating habits might bring them. Having escaped the infection himself, he was quite willing, apparently, to leave the rest to chance. It was, he had been told, very prevalent, but personally he had not come across it. And so he continued to interest himself in bacteriology, through which fame, wealth, and title had come to him.

As I left his consulting-room I felt as though I had just emerged from the Middle Ages, and from listening to the discourse of some learned theologian—a marvellous expert in the doctrine of the Incarnation and the Procession of the Holy Spirit, but still believing that the sun went round the earth, and that the earth was flat; and though—God aiding him—he would put to death any who thought otherwise, the subject did not interest him!

He remains to me a portentous example of how a really brilliant mind can totter into second infancy when called upon to dig for the roots of knowledge outside his own cabbage-patch in hitherto uncultivated ground.

What led me to this strange scientific experience was very much to the point. For it was just then, ten years ago, that I had been asked to join a society having for its object the formation of a more intelligent and less servile public opinion on this and various other difficult sex problems which are a part of human nature. I agreed to do so upon one condition— that membership should be open to men and women on equal terms, and that women should be upon the executive committee. Even in that comparatively enlightened group the proposal seemed revolutionary; and I was asked whether I realized that such things as homo-sexuality would have to be openly discussed. My answer was: "That is why we must include women." I contended that where a problem concerns both sexes alike, only by the full co-operation of both sexes can it be rightly solved.

My contention was admitted to be sound, and the society was formed on the equal basis I had advocated; and perhaps one of its best discoveries is that, in a body of social goodwill, there is no such thing as "the unmentionable." Since then, women have been called to juries, and it has become a duty of good citizenship for them to share with men the knowledge of things which the obscurantists, in order to keep them as a male perquisite, chose to describe as "unmentionable."

"E pur se muove": that wise old saying continues to have its application in every age. Always, at some contentious point in the affairs of men, belief in knowledge and belief in ignorance stand as antagonists. The nineteenth century had its superstitions, quite as much as the sixteenth and the seventeenth centuries, when loyalty to the Mosaic law made the persecution of witchcraft a religious duty. And a surviving superstition of our own time has been that false and foolish moral insistence on regarding certain maladjustments of nature as something too horrible to be mentioned, and of putting the victims thereof in a class apart, rather lower than the ordinary criminal. The old theological idea that the world was flat reproduced itself in another form; and so, in spite of the advance of science, the moral world had to remain flat and simple, unencumbered by nature-problems, for fear of the terrible things it might have to contain and account for if once admitted to be round.

Twentieth-century science is busy proving to us that the moral world is dangerously round; and it is no use trying to fall off it by walking about it with shut eyes. From a flat world that method of escape might be conceivably possible, but not from a round. A round world has us in its grip; and it is our duty as intelligent human beings to face the danger and get used to it.

What a strange irony of life that the man who tried most to detach himself from the unlovely complications of modern civilization should have become the symbol, or the byword, of one of its least solved problems; and that society's blind resentment toward a phenomenon it had not the patience or the charity to trace to its origin, should have supplied him so savagely with that "complete life of the artist" which success could never have given him.